Piano Playbook

CW01023854

SMOOTH JAZZ

47 jazz standards for piano. From the cool sounds of
Charlie Parker to the Latin rhythms of the samba!

Published by
Wise Publications, 14-15 Berners Street, London W1T 3LJ, UK.

Exclusive Distributors:
Music Sales Limited, Distribution Centre, Newmarket Road, Bury St Edmunds, Suffolk IP33 3YB, UK.
Music Sales Pty Limited , Units 3-4, 17 Willfox Street, Condell Park, NSW 2200, Australia.

Order No. AM1006687
ISBN: 978-1-78305-131-1
This book © Copyright 2013 Wise Publications, a division of Music Sales Limited.

Cover design by Fresh Lemon.
Compiled and edited by Sam Lung.
Music processed by Paul Ewers Music Design.
Introductory text by Graham Vickers.
Cover photograph by John Cohen/Getty Images.
Page 4 photograph by Michael Ochs Archives/Getty Images.

Printed in the EU.

Your Guarantee of Quality
As publishers, we strive to produce every book to the highest commercial standards.
This book has been carefully designed to minimise awkward page turns and to make playing
from it a real pleasure. Particular care has been given to specifying acid-free, neutral-sized
paper made from pulps which have not been elemental chlorine bleached. This pulp is from
farmed sustainable forests and was produced with special regard for the environment.
Throughout, the printing and binding have been planned to ensure a sturdy, attractive publication
which should give years of enjoyment. If your copy fails to meet our high standards,
please inform us and we will gladly replace it.

www.musicsales.com

WISE PUBLICATIONS
part of The Music Sales Group
London / New York / Paris / Sydney / Copenhagen / Berlin / Madrid / Hong Kong / Tokyo

CONTENTS

SMOOTH JAZZ

Jazz, an original American art form, is sometimes thought of as a 'difficult' music genre composed and played by driven men dismissive of the clichés of the mainstream. While it is true that someone like John Coltrane often seemed to make a virtue out of inaccessibility, Charlie Parker could play the remote intellectual and Artie Shaw was a self-proclaimed 'very difficult man', one of jazz's greatest assets has always been the vitality it has lent to popular genres.

Hoagy Carmichael became a star through writing, singing and playing piano songs that were very jazz-influenced while still being radio-friendly. 'Georgia On My Mind' and 'Stardust' are surely two of the greatest popular songs ever written. Carmichael often popped up in supporting movie roles, usually playing piano in a bar that had seen better days and occasionally delivering a laconic line or two on the margins of the main action. Dave Brubeck's 'Take Five' was also a popular chart success despite — or perhaps because of — its wilful 5/4 time signature, something pianist Brubeck and his alto saxophonist Paul Desmond had been prompted to try after hearing Turkish musicians play in some even more recondite time signature. George Shearing, a blind, Battersea-born jazz pianist, also hit the big time in 1952 with his instrumental version of 'Lullaby Of Birdland', its title a reference to Charlie Parker's New York club and its jazzy feel appealing to singers ranging from Ella Fitzgerald to Amy Winehouse.

Charlie Parker himself, known as the Bird, was a brilliant jazz saxophonist and his number 'Ornithology' demonstrates his love of fast tempos, virtuosity and improvisation while at the same time perhaps identifying him as one of those serious jazzmen who never welcomed dilettante fans.

The album *Jazz Samba* (1962) marked arrival of Latin-flavoured jazz in the States. Stan Getz was the star and Brazilian composer Antonio Carlos Jobim wrote two of its most famous songs whose titles amusingly seemed to advertise their limitations: "Desafinado" (Slightly Out of Tune) and "Samba de Uma Nota Só" (One-Note Samba).

Closer to jazz's roots was Harlem-born Fats Waller whose joyous stride piano technique had the virtue of sounding easy even though it wasn't. His sublime piano skills combined with a larger-than-life personality to produce immensely popular piano jazz hits like 'Ain't Misbehavin''.

Neal Hefti was a prodigious musical talent who played trumpet for Woody Herman and later made his name as an arranger before diversifying into compositions as unlikely as the TV *Batman* theme and the signature music for both the movie and TV series of Neil Simon's *The Odd Couple*. He proved a particularly simpatico arranger for pianist and organist Count Basie and his arrangement of his own composition 'Li'l Darlin' for Basie was a particular popular success. But perhaps one of the all-time greatest jazz pieces to win popular acclaim is 'Take The 'A' Train' written by Billy Strayhorn for Duke Ellington. Its title was famously taken from Ellington's scribbled instructions as to how Strayhorn might find his address, a story embellished over the years so that it eventually became a celebration of the route by which black jazz musicians, who usually lived in Harlem, travelled to gigs in cosmopolitan mid-town Manhattan. Perhaps that was the better story, somehow echoing the birth of jazz which came about when black American music met white European musical forms to produce a satisfyingly vigorous offspring, sometimes lusty but often velvet smooth.

Adios

Words by Eddie Woods
Music by Enric Madriguera

Moderately

We were so hap - py dear___ to - geth - er,___ and ev - 'ry
Ya la a - le - gri - a de___ mi vi - da es co - mou_n

dream of joy___ we knew,___ a cas - tle in the air,___ dear, for -
sue - ño que___ se vá___ por - que_all lle - gar de nue - vo el

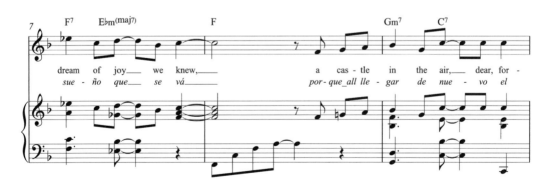

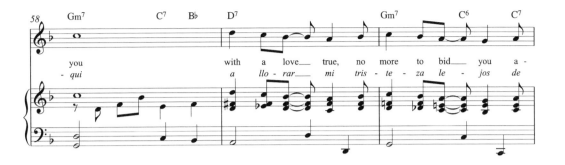

you / -qui

with a love___ true, no more to bid___ you a-
a llo - rar___ mi tris - te - za le - jos de

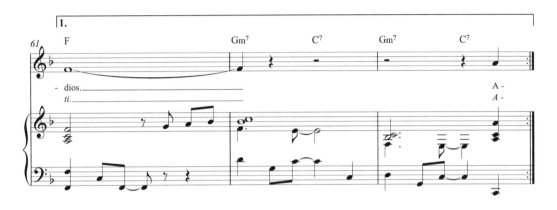

1.

- dios.___
ti.___

A-
A-

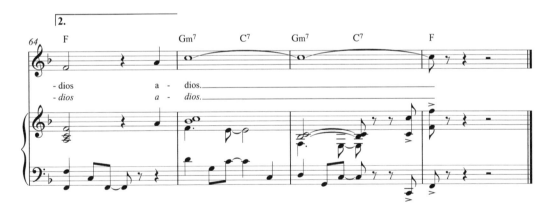

2.

- dios a - dios.___
- dios a - dios.___

Additional verse:
Of all the words that bring us sadness
There's none so hopeless as goodbye
And so, although it may be just madness
Maybe we'll meet dear, by and by.

Then we'll recall the tender yearnings
That in the past we used to know
The memories will soon be returning
To set our longing hearts all aglow.

Água De Beber

(Drinking Water)

Words by Norman Gimbel
Music by Antonio Carlos Jobim

Moderately

Your love___ is rain,

Portuguese Lyrics:
Eu quis amar, mas tive medo
E quis salvar meu corração
Mas o amor sabe um segredo
O medo pode matar seu corração.

Água de Beber
Água de Beber camará
Água de Beber
Água de Beber camará.

Eu nunca fiz coisa tão certa
Entrei pra escola do perdão
A minha casa vive aberta
Abre todas as portas do corração.

Água de Beber *etc.*

Eu sempre tive uma certeza
Que só me deu desilusão
É que o amor É uma tristeza
Muita mágoa demais para um corração.

Água de Beber *etc.*

Amor

Words by Ricardo Lopez Mendez
Music by Gabriel Ruiz

Ain't Misbehavin'

Words by Andy Razaf
Music by Thomas 'Fats' Waller & Harry Brooks

24

Bésame Mucho

(Kiss Me Much)

Words & Music by Consuelo Velazquez

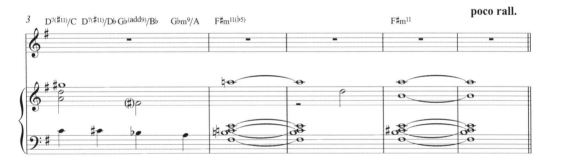

Bé - sa - me, bé - sa - me__ mu - cho,__

Co - mo si fue-ra es-ta no-che la úl-ti-ma vez;__

Bé - sa - me,__ bé - sa - me mu - cho,__

Que ten-go mie - do perder-te__ te, per-der-

76 Em⁷ ... Em/D ... A⁷⁽♭⁹⁾/C♯

-ten-go mie-do_____ per - der - te,

79 F♯m⁷⁽♭⁵⁾/C ... B⁷ Em¹¹

D.S. al Coda

per - der - te____ des - pués._____

Coda

82 F♯m⁷⁽♭⁵⁾/C ... B⁷⁽♯⁹⁾ ... Em¹¹ ... Em⁹/D

Quie - ro sin-ce-re - te____ muy cer - ca, Mi - rar-me en tus
(Original Spanish version: te - ner - te____)

86 F♯m⁷⁽♭⁵⁾/C ... B⁷⁽♯⁹⁾ ... Em¹¹ ... Am/E

o - jos, ver - te jun - to a mí,_____ pien - sa que

30

tal vez ma-ña-na yo ya es-ta-ré le-jos, muy le-jos de

Lazily

ti._____ Bé - sa - me, bé - sa - me_____

_____ mu - cho,_____ co-mo si fue-ra es-ta no-che la úl-ti -

- ma vez; Bé - sa - me,_____ bé - sa -

33

Black Coffee

Words & Music by Paul Francis Webster & Sonny Burke

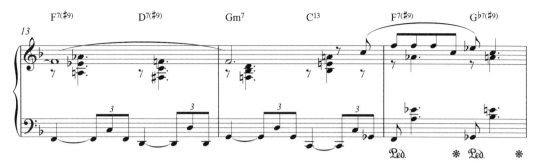

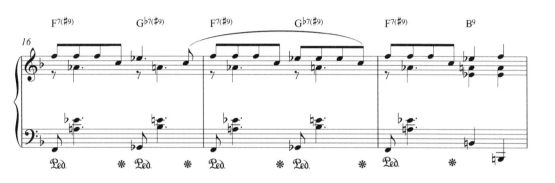

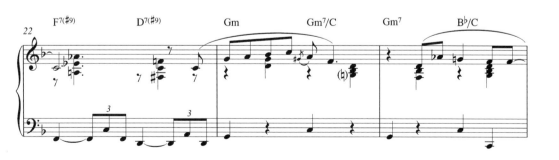

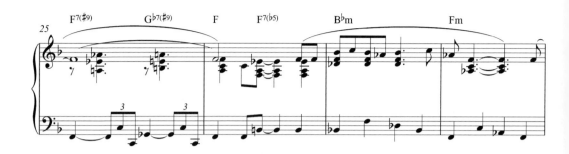

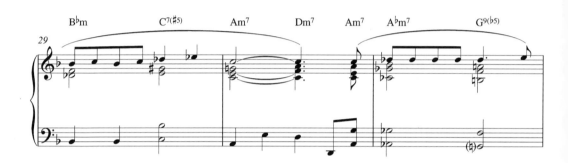

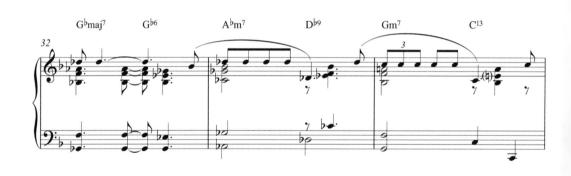

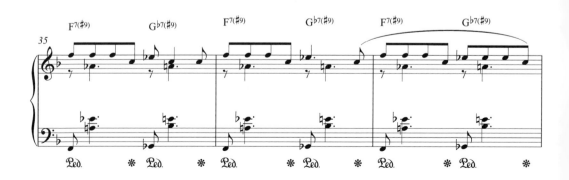

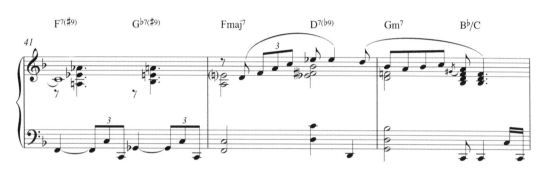

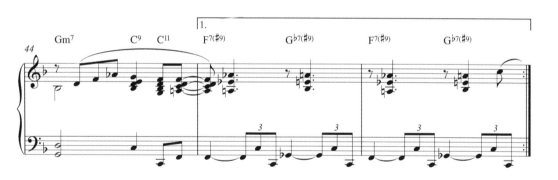

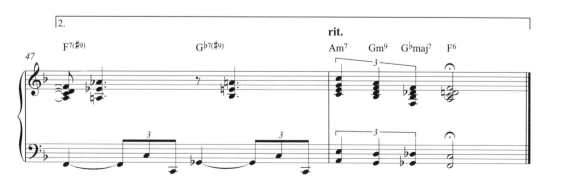

Blue Bossa

Music by Kenny Dorham

Corcovado

(Quiet Nights Of Quiet Stars)

Words & Music by Antonio Carlos Jobim & Giorgio Calabrese

Steadily and gently ♩ = 63

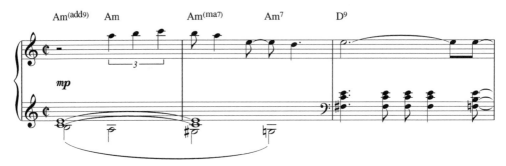

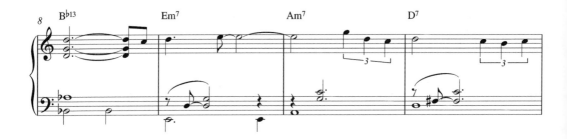

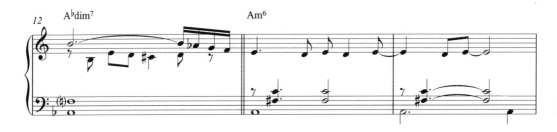

Chelsea Bridge

Music by Billy Strayhorn

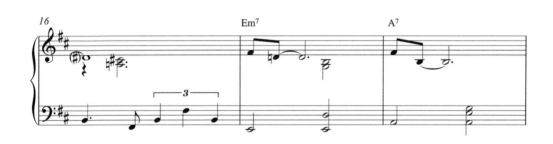

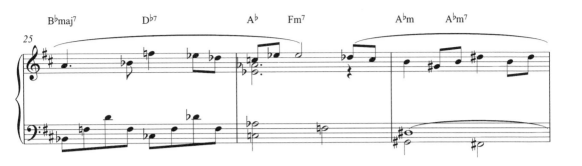

Desafinado

(Slightly Out Of Tune)

Words & Music by Newton Mendonca & Antonio Carlos Jobim

Medium Bossa Nova ♩ = 69

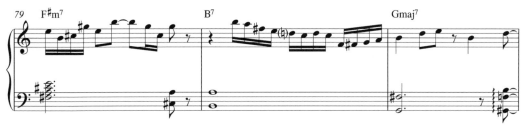

Dindi

Words by Aloysio de Oliveira
Music by Antonio Carlos Jobim

Moderately

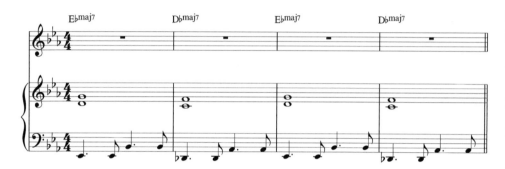

Sky, so vast is the sky with far a - way clouds just wan - der - ing by,

where do they go? _____ Oh, I don't know, don't know.

Oh, Din - di, like the song of the wind in the trees, that's how my heart is sing - ing, Din - di, hap - py Din - di, when you're with me. I love you more each day, yes I do, yes I do.

Footprints

Music by Wayne Shorter

Fly Me To The Moon (In Other Words)

Words & Music by Bart Howard

Frenesi

Music by Alberto Dominguez

(with a bounce)

God Bless The Child

Words & Music by Billie Holiday & Arthur Herzog Jr.

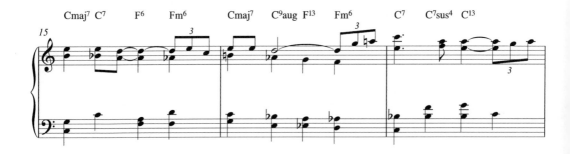

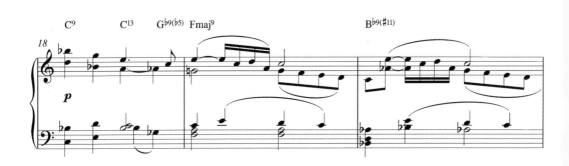

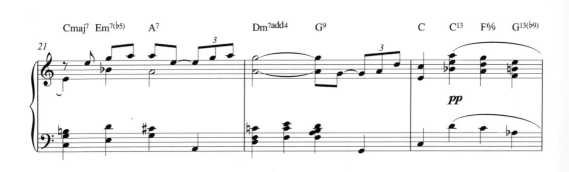

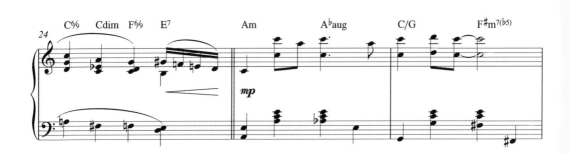

Georgia On My Mind

Words by Stuart Gorrell
Music by Hoagy Carmichael

The Girl From Ipanema

(Garota De Ipanema)

Words by Vinicius De Moraes
Music by Antonio Jobim

Li'l Darlin'

Music by Neal Hefti

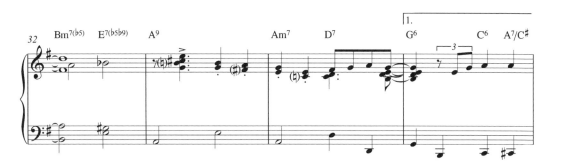

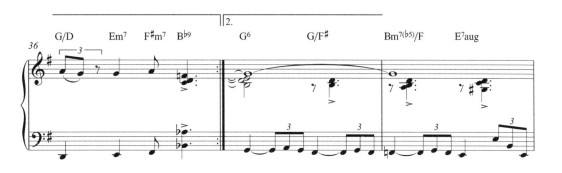

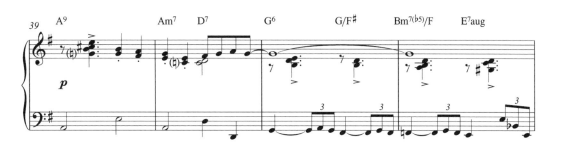

Here's That Rainy Day

Words & Music by Johnny Burke & Jimmy Van Heusen

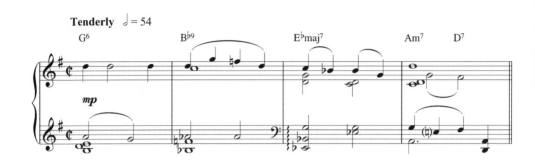

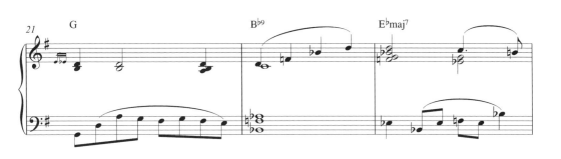

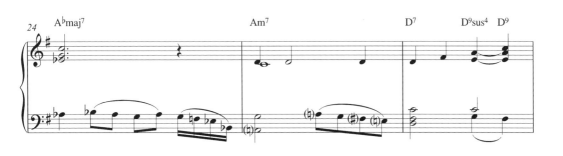

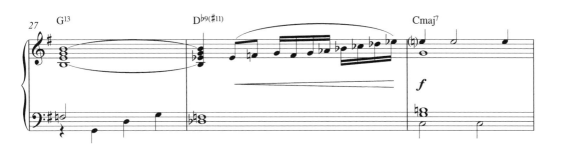

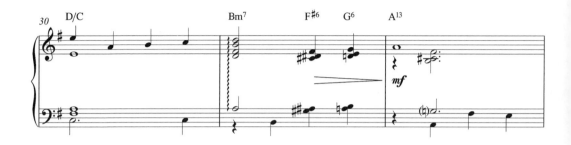

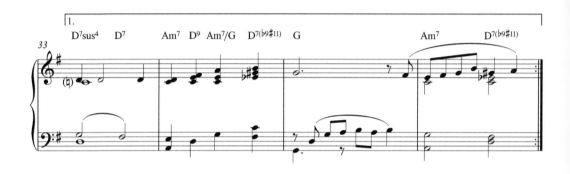

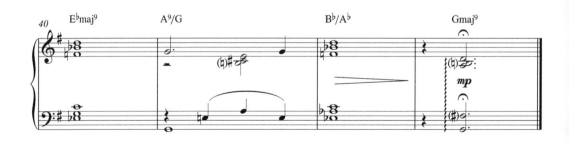

How Insensitive

Words by Vinicius De Moraes
Music by Antonio Carlos Jobim

Moderately

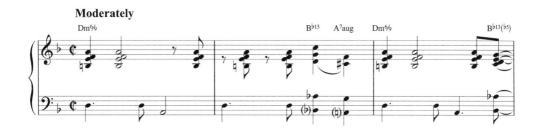

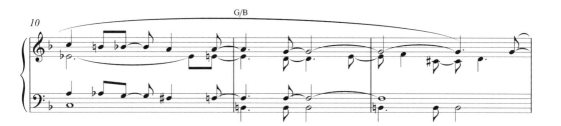

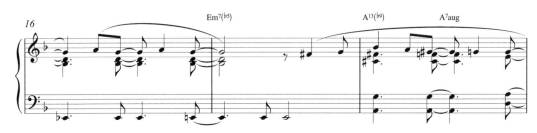

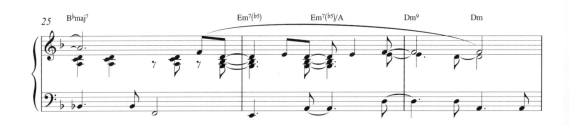

In Her Family

Music by Pat Metheny

Freely (♩ = c.76 ma molto rubato)

In Your Own Sweet Way

Music by Dave Brubeck

Moderate

In the style of a waltz

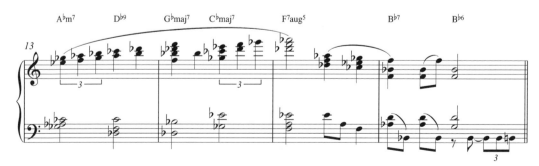

In the style of a waltz

Lullaby Of Birdland

Words by George David Weiss
Music by George Shearing

Moderately with a beat

Mas Que Nada

(Say No More)

Words & Music by Jorge Ben

Bright beguine tempo

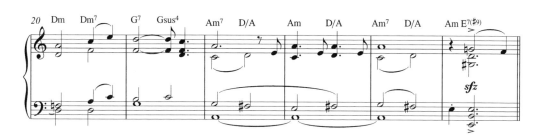

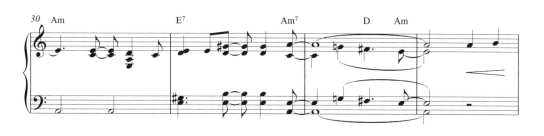

Monk's Mood

Music by Thelonious Monk

Misty

Words & Music by Erroll Garner & Johnny Burke

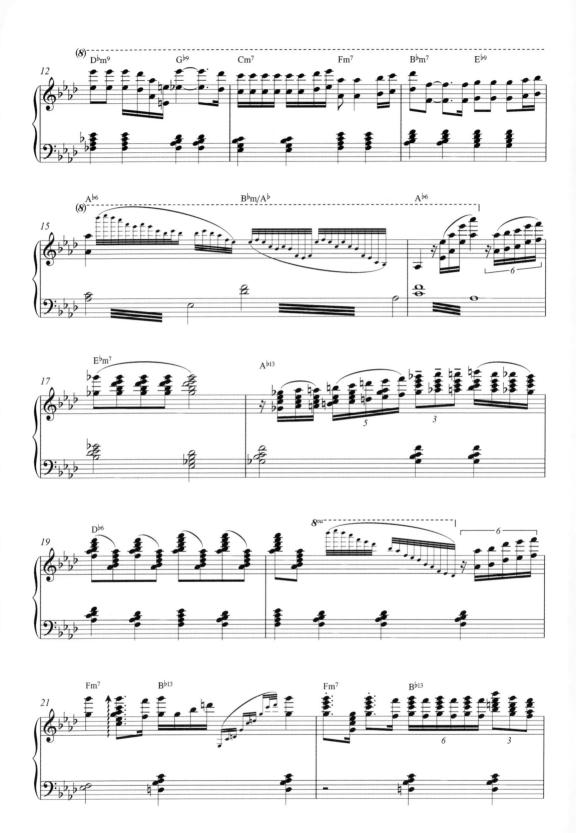

A Night In Tunisia

Words by Raymond Leveen
Music by Dizzy Gillespie & Frank Paparelli

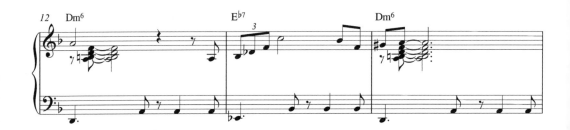

One Note Samba

(Samba De Uma Nota Só)

Words by Newton Mendonca
Music by Antonio Carlos Jobim

To Coda ⊕

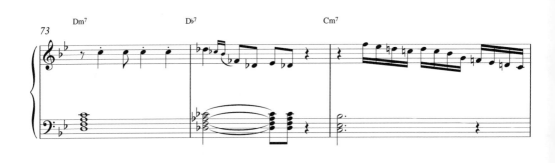

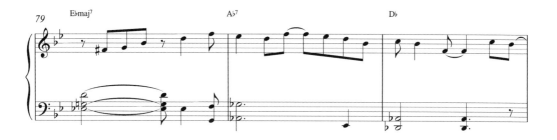

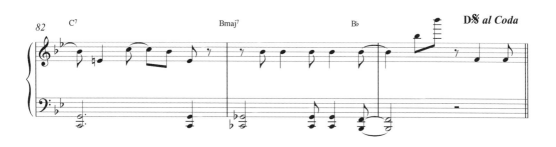

Ornithology

Music by Charlie Parker & Benny Harris

Perhaps, Perhaps, Perhaps

(Quizas, Quizas, Quizas)

Words & Music by Osvaldo Farres

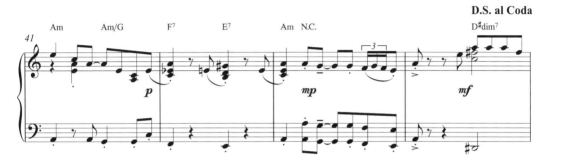

D.S. al Coda

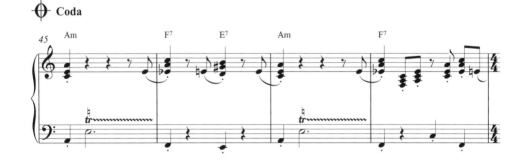

Coda

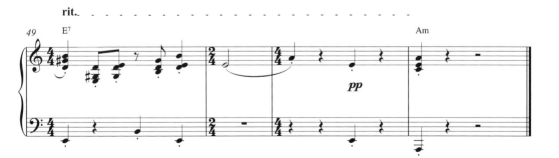

Perdido

Words by Ervin Drake & Harry Lenk
Music by Juan Tizol

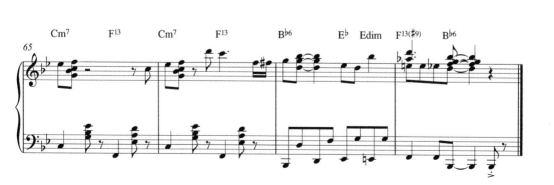

Poinciana

Words by Buddy Bernier
Music by Nat Simon

Moderately, with expression

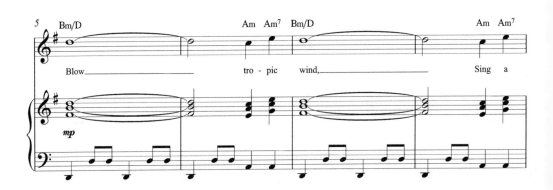

Blow_____ tro - pic wind,_____ Sing a

song_____ thru the tree._____

131

Quiet Now

Words & Music by Denny Zeitlin

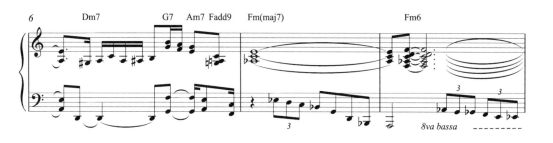

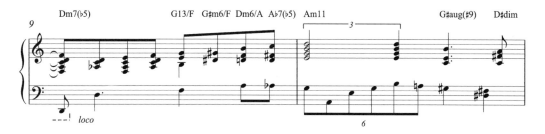

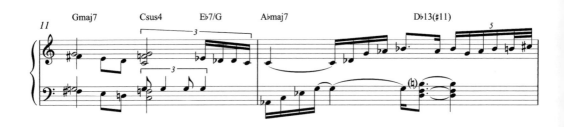

A tempo (medium slow)

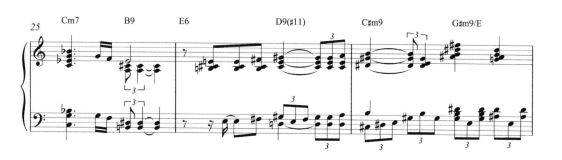

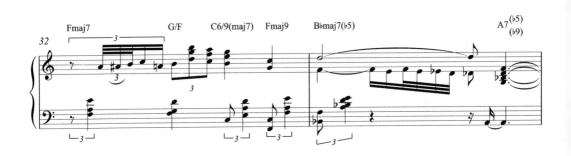

Solitude

Words by Eddie De Lange & Irving Mills
Music by Duke Ellington

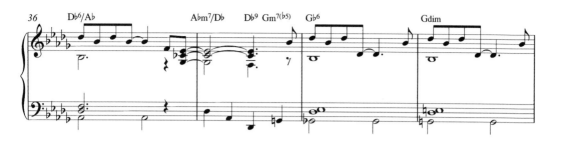

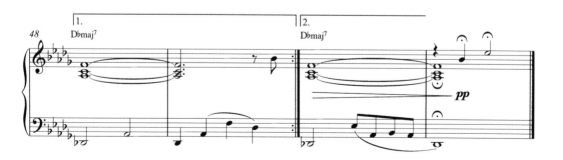

So Nice (Summer Samba)

Words by Norman Gimbel & Paulo Sergio Valle
Music by Marcos Valle

Stardust

Words by Mitchell Parish
Music by Hoagy Carmichael

Song For My Father

Music by Horace Silver

to Coda ⊕

Straight No Chaser

Music by Thelonious Monk

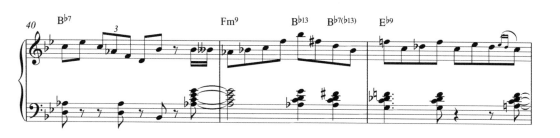

Sway
(Quién Será)

Words & Music by Pablo Beltran Ruiz & Luis Demetrio Traconis Molina

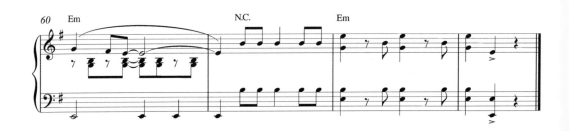

When Sunny Gets Blue

Words by Jack Segal
Music by Marvin Fisher

Moderately slow

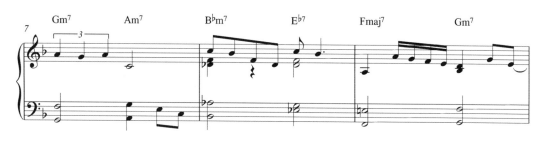

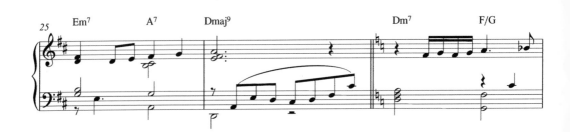

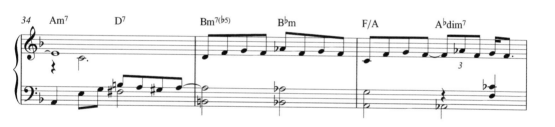

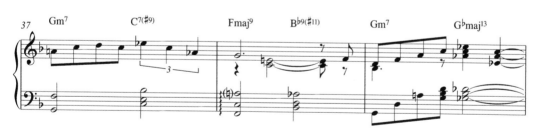

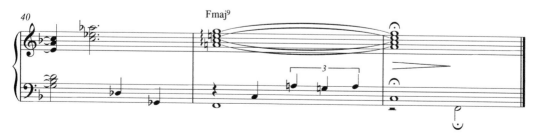

Take Five

Music by Paul Desmond

to Coda

163

Take The 'A' Train

Words & Music by Billy Strayhorn

The Tokyo Blues

Words & Music by Horace Silver

D.C. al Coda
(with repeat)

175

Two Lonely People

Words & Music by Bill Evans & Carol Hall

Medium 'ballad' tempo
Freely, espress.

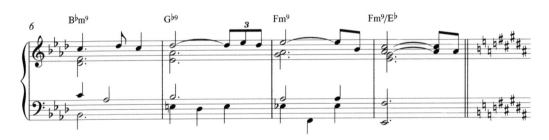

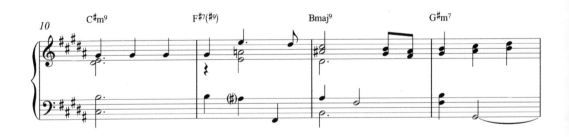

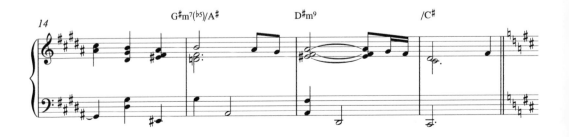

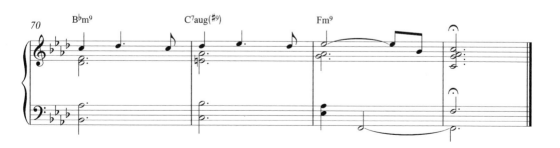

Wave

Words & Music by Antonio Carlos Jobim

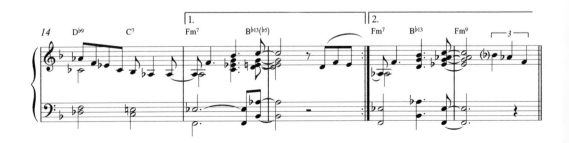

Without You

(Tres Palabras)

Words & Music by Osvaldo Farres
Translated by Ray Gilbert

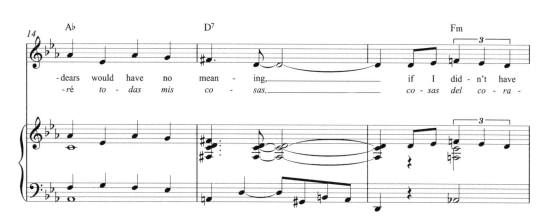

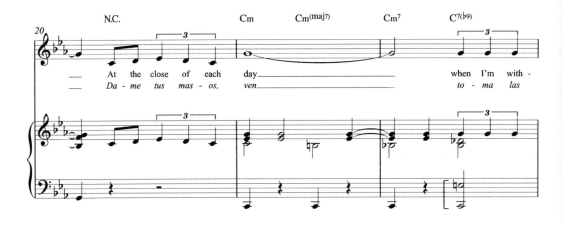

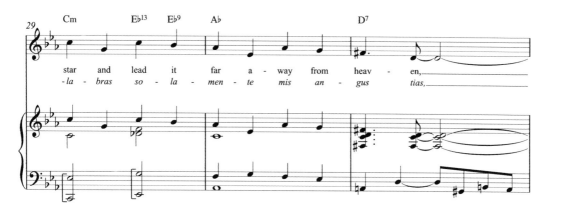

185

Waltz For Debby

Words by Gene Lees
Music by Bill Evans

187